THE CRUCIFIXION

THE CRUCIFIXION

A MEDITATION

ON THE

SACRED PASSION OF THE HOLY REDEEMER

FOR TWO SOLO VOICES (TENOR AND BASS) AND CHORUS, AND
INTERSPERSED WITH HYMNS TO BE SUNG BY THE CONGREGATION

THE WORDS SELECTED AND WRITTEN BY THE

Rev. J. SPARROW-SIMPSON. M.A.

THE MUSIC BY

J. STAINER.

REVISED EDITION.

NOVELLO & CO LTD

Borough Green   Sevenoaks   Kent
London: 27 Soho Square, W1

THE CRUCIFIXION.

RECIT.—AND THEY CAME TO A PLACE NAMED GETHSEMANE.

And they came to a place nam - ed Geth - se - ma - ne, and Je - sus

saith to His dis - ci - ples: Sit ye here, while I shall

pray.

THE CRUCIFIXION

No. 2. THE AGONY.

Bass. Andante.

Could ye not watch with Me one brief hour? Could ye not pi - ty My sor - est need? Ah! if ye sleep while the tem - pests lower, sure - ly, My friends, I am lone in - deed.

CHORUS.

Soprano.
Je - su, Lord Je - su, bowed in bit - ter an - guish, and bear - ing all the

Alto.
Je - su, Lord Je - su, bowed in bit - ter an - guish, and bear - ing all the

Tenor.
Je - su, Lord Je - su, bowed in bit - ter an - guish, and bear - ing all the

Bass.
Je - su, Lord Je - su, bowed in bit - ter an - guish, and bear - ing all the

e - vil we .. have done, Oh, teach us, teach us how to love Thee for

e - vil we .. have done, Oh, teach us, teach us how to love Thee for

e - vil we .. have done, Oh, teach us, teach us how to love Thee for

e - vil we .. have done, Oh, teach us, teach us how to love Thee for

Thy love; Help us to pray, and watch, and mourn with Thee.

Thy love; Help us to pray, and watch, and mourn with Thee.

Thy love; Help us to pray, and watch, and mourn with Thee.

Thy love; Help us to pray, and watch, and mourn with Thee.

SOLO.

Could ye not watch with Me one brief hour? Did ye not say up-on

Ke - dron's slope, Ye would not fall in - to the Tempt - er's

power? Did ye not mur - mur great words of hope?

Chorus.

Je - su, Lord Je - su, bowed in bit - ter an - guish, and bear - ing all the

Je - su, Lord Je - su, bowed in bit - ter an - guish, and bear - ing all the

Je - su, Lord Je - su, bowed in bit - ter an - guish, and bear - ing all the

Je - su, Lord Je - su, bowed in bit - ter an - guish, and bear - ing all the

e - vil we .. have done, Oh, teach us, teach us how to love Thee for

e - vil we .. have done, Oh, teach us, teach us how to love Thee for

e - vil we .. have done, Oh, teach us, teach us how to love Thee for

e - vil we .. have done, Oh, teach us, teach us how to love Thee for

Thy love, Help us to pray, and watch, and mourn with Thee.

Thy love, Help us to pray, and watch, and mourn with Thee.

Thy love, Help us to pray, and watch, and mourn with Thee.

Thy love, Help us to pray, and watch, and mourn with Thee.

Solo. *(ad lib.)* *a tempo.* *mf*

Could ye not watch with Me? e - ven so: Will - ing in

heart, but the flesh .. is vain. Back to Mine ag - o - ny

I .. must go, Lone - ly to pray in bit - ter - est pain.

Allegro.

TENOR.

And they laid their hands on Him, and took Him, and led Him a-way to the high priest. And the high priest ask-ed Him and said un-to Him, Art Thou the Christ, the Son of the Bless-ed? Je-sus said, I am: and ye shall

Allegro. ♩=120.

Full Sw.

cres.

ad lib.

f

Slow.
BASS (*a voice in the Choir*).

mf

TENOR. BASS SOLO. *Slow.* *cres.*

Slow.

p *cres.*

see the Son of man sit-ting on the right hand of power, and

cres.   cres.

com - ing in.. the.. clouds of heaven.

cres.   f   colla voce.

TENOR.
Allegro molto.

Then the high priest

Allegro molto.

BASS
(one of the Choir).

rent . . . . his clothes, and saith: What need

rit.   rit.

TENOR.
Slow.

we a - ny further wit - ness-es? Ye have heard the blas-phe-my. And they all con -

Slow.

p   p

a tempo.

p

- demned Him to be guilt - y of death. And they bound

pp   pp   p a tempo.

Adagio. cres.

Je - sus and car-ried Him a - way, and de - liv-ered Him to Pi - late. And

REOIT. *Moderato. dim. a tempo.*

Pi - late will - ing to con - tent the peo - ple, re - leas - ed Bar - ra - bas un - to

them, and de - liv - ered Je - sus, when he had scourg - ed Him, to be

cru - ci - fied. And the sol - diers led Him a - way.

Attacca.

CUT TO TEMPO 1mo

No. 3.   PROCESSIONAL TO CALVARY.

rall.
Solo.
p
Sw.
Ped.
cres.
dim.
p Sw.
senza Ped.
rall.
cres. molto.
Tempo 1mo.
f Gt.
Ped.
cres.

Fling wide the gates! fling wide the gates! fling wide the

Fling wide the gates! fling wide the gates! fling wide the

Fling wide the gates! fling wide the gates! fling wide the

Fling wide the gates! fling wide the gates!

gates! fling wide the gates!

gates! fling wide the gates!

gates! fling wide the gates! fling wide the

fling wide the gates! fling wide the gates!

Tuba.

poco rit. *Tempo 1mo. pomposo.*

fling wide the gates! fling wide the gates!.. fling wide the gates! for the

fling wide the gates! fling wide the gates! fling wide the gates! for the

poco rit. *Tempo 1mo.*

gates! fling wide the gates! fling wide the gates! for the

poco rit. *Tempo 1mo.*

fling wide the gates! fling wide the gates! for the

Tempo 1mo.

Gt. *Tuba.* *poco rit.* *Gt.* *pomposo.*

Sa-viour waits To tread in His roy-al way; He has come from a-bove, in His power and love, To die on this Pas-sion day. Fling wide the gates! the Sa-viour waits! Fling wide the gates! fling wide the waits! He

gates ! the Sa - viour waits .. To tread in His roy - al way, Fling wide the

gates ! the Sa - viour waits ! Fling wide the gates !

waits, the Sa - viour waits .. To tread in His roy - al way, Fling wide the

waits, the Sa - viour waits ! Fling wide the gates !

rall. cres. *ff* *Tempo 1mo. pomposo.* *f*

gates ! He waits, the Sa - viour waits ! .. Fling wide the gates ! for the

rall. cres. *ff* *Tempo 1mo.* *f*

fling wide the gates ! He waits, the Sa - viour waits ! Fling wide the gates ! for the

rall. cres. *ff* *Tempo 1mo.* *f*

gates ! He waits, the Sa - viour waits ! Fling wide the gates ! for the

rall. cres. *ff* *Tempo 1mo.*

fling wide the gates ! He waits, the Sa - viour waits ! Fling wide the gates ! for the

rall. cres. *ff* *f pomposo.*

dim.

Sa - viour waits To tread in His roy - al way ; He has come from a - bove in His

dim.

Sa - viour waits To tread in His roy - al way ; .. He has come from a - bove in His

dim.

Sa - viour waits To tread in His roy - al way ; .. He has come from a - bove in His

dim.

Sa - viour waits To tread in His roy - al way ; He has come from a - bove in His

dim.

power and love, To die on this Pas-sion day.

power and love, To die on this Pas-sion day. His Cross is the sign of a

power and love, To die on this Pas-sion day.

power and love, To die on this Pas-sion day. His Cross is the sign of a

His crown is the thorn-wreath of woe, . . He bears His load on the

love di-vine, His crown is the thorn-wreath of woe, . .

His crown is the thorn-wreath of woe, . .

love di-vine, His crown is the thorn-wreath of woe, . .

senza Ped.

sor-row-ful road. Fling wide the gates ! fling wide the gates !

Fling wide the gates ! fling wide the

And bends 'neath the bur-den low, Fling wide the gates !

And bends 'neath the bur-den low, Fling wide the gates !

Full Sw.

poco accel. cres.

Ped. in 8ves.

fling wide the gates! the Sa - viour waits! . .

gates! fling wide the gates! He waits, the Sa - viour waits! . .

fling wide the gates! He waits, the Sa - viour waits!

fling wide the gates! fling wide the gates! He waits, the Sa - viour waits!

cres.

fling wide the gates! fling wide the gates! the Sa - viour waits . . To

fling wide the gates! fling wide the gates! the Sa - viour waits!

fling wide the gates! fling wide the gates! He waits, the Sa - viour waits . . To

fling wide the gates! fling wide the gates! He waits, the Sa - viour waits!

mf Gt.

rall. cres.

tread in His roy - al way; Fling wide the gates! He waits, the Sa - viour

rall. cres.

fling wide the gates! fling wide the gates! He waits, the Sa - viour

rall. cres.

tread in His roy - al way; Fling wide the gates! He waits, the Sa - viour

rall. cres.

fling wide the gates! fling wide the gates! He waits, the Sa - viour

rall. cres.

Tempo 1mo. pomposo.

waits!.. Fling wide the gates! for the Sa - viour waits To tread in His roy - al

waits! Fling wide the gates! for the Sa - viour waits To tread in His roy - al

waits! Fling wide the gates! for the Sa - viour waits To tread in His roy - al

waits! Fling wide the gates! for the Sa - viour waits To tread in His roy - al

f pomposo.

way, He has come from a-bove in His power and love To die on this Pas - sion

way, ... He has come from a-bove in His power and love To die on this Pas - sion

way, .. He has come from a-bove in His power and love To die on this Pas - sion

way, He has come from a-bove in His power and love To die on this Pas - sion

day, to die on this Pas - sion day.

day, ... to die on this Pas - sion day.

day, to die on this Pas - sion day.

day, ... this Pas - - sion day.

senza Ped.

TENOR SOLO.

How sweet is the grace of His sa - cred Face And love - - ly be - - yond com - pare;

pp

poco rit.

Solo.

p tempo.

poco rit.

Ped.

colla voce.

Though wea - ry and worn with the mer - ci - less scorn Of a world He has come .. to spare. The bur - den of wrong that earth bears a - long, Past e - vil, and e - vil to be,— All sins of man since the world be - gan, They are laid, dear Lord, on Thee.

Thee.

Tempo 1mo. CHORUS. *cres.*

Then on to the end, my God and my Friend, With Thy ban - ner lift - ed

Then on to the end, my God and my Friend, With Thy ban - ner lift - ed

Then on to the end, my God and my Friend, With Thy ban - ner lift - ed

Then on to the end, my God and my Friend, With Thy ban - ner lift - ed

Tempo 1mo.

p | *Gt.*   *cres.*

high! Then on to the end, my God and my Friend, With Thy ban - ner lift - ed

high! Then on to the end, my God and my Friend, With Thy ban - ner lift - ed

high! Then on to the end, my God and my Friend, With Thy ban - ner lift - ed

high! Then on to the end, my God and my Friend, With Thy ban - ner lift - ed

cres.   *f*

high, Thou art come from a-bove, in Thy power and love, To en-dure and suf-fer and

high, Thou art come from a-bove, in Thy power and love, To en-dure and suf-fer and

high, Thou art come from a-bove, in Thy power and love, To en-dure and suf-fer and

high, Thou art come from a-bove, in Thy power and love, To en-dure and suf - fer.

die. Fling wide the gates! the Sa - viour waits! . .

die. Fling wide the gates! He waits, the Sa - viour waits! . .

die. Fling wide the gates! He waits, the Sa - viour waits!

Fling wide the gates! fling wide the gates! He waits, the Sa - viour waits!

fling wide the gates! fling wide the gates! the Sa - viour waits! . . Then

fling wide the gates! fling wide the gates! the Sa - viour waits! Then

fling wide the gates! fling wide the gates! He waits, the Sa - viour waits! Then

fling wide the gates! fling wide the gates! He waits, the Sa - viour waits! Then on to the end, my God and my Friend, To suf - fer, en - dure and die, ... to

on to the end, my God and my Friend, To suf - fer, en - dure and die, ... to

on to the end, my God and my Friend, To suf - fer, en - dure and die, ... to

on to the end, my God and my Friend, To suf - fer, en - dure and die, ... to

suf - fer, en - dure and die.

suf - fer en - dure and die.

suf - fer, en - dure and die.

suf - fer, en - dure and die.

STANO.

Ped. 16 ft. only.

No. 4.   Recit.—AND WHEN THEY WERE COME. *Allit.*

With expression.
Bass. (*ad lib.*)

And   when   they   had   come   to   the   place   call - ed

With expression. ♩ = 60.

p   *p*

senza Ped.

Cal - va - ry,   there   they   cru - ci - fied   Him,   they   cru - ci - fied   Him,   and   the

mal - e - fac - tors,   one   on   the   right,   and   the   o - ther   on   the

left.

pp

rall.

Attacca.

8002.

No. 5.   THE MYSTERY OF THE DIVINE HUMILIATION.

To be sung by the Choir and Congregation.

Cross of Jesus, Cross of Sorrow,
 Where the Blood of Christ was shed,
Perfect man on thee was tortured,
 Perfect God on thee has bled.

Here the King of all the ages,
 Throned in light ere worlds could be
Robed in mortal flesh is dying,
 Crucified by sin for me.

O mysterious condescending!
 O abandonment sublime!
Very God Himself is bearing
 All the sufferings of time!

Evermore for human failure
 By His Passion we can plead;
God has borne all mortal anguish,
 Surely He will know our need.

This—all human thought surpassing—
 This is earth's most awful hour,
God has taken mortal weakness!
 God has laid aside His Power!

Once the Lord of brilliant seraphs,
 Winged with Love to do His Will,
Now the scorn of all His creatures,
 And the aim of every ill.

Up in Heaven, sublimest glory
 Circled round Him from the first;
But the earth finds none to serve Him,
 None to quench His raging thirst.

Who shall fathom that descending,
 From the rainbow-circled throne,
Down to earth's most base profaning,
 Dying desolate alone.

From the "Holy, Holy, Holy,
 We adore Thee, O most High,"
Down to earth's blaspheming voices
 And the shout of "Crucify."

Cross of Jesus, Cross of Sorrow,
 Where the Blood of Christ was shed
Perfect man on thee was tortured,
 Perfect God on thee has bled.

No. 6. RECIT.—HE MADE HIMSELF OF NO REPUTATION.

Andante. Bass.

He made Him-self of no rep-u-ta-tion, and took up-

- -on Him the form of a ser-vant, and was made in the like-ness of

men: And be-ing found in fashion as a man, He hum-bled Him-

- -self, He hum-bled Him-self, and be-came o-be-dient un-to death, ev'n the

death of the Cross.

No. 7.

THE MAJESTY OF THE DIVINE HUMILIATION.

Moderato.
TENOR SOLO.

King ev - er glo - rious, King ev - er glo - rious! The dews of

death are ga - th'ring round Thee; Up - on the Cross Thy foes have bound Thee— Thy

strength is gone, Thy strength is gone. Not in Thy

Ma - jes - ty, Robed in Heaven's su - prem-est splen-dour, But in weak - ness and sur -

-ren - - der, Thou hang - est here.

Who can be like Thee? Pi-late high in Zi-on

dwell - ing, Rome with arms the world com-pel - ling, Proud though they be?

Thou art sub - lime, Thou art sub - lime: Far more

aw - ful in Thy weak-ness, More than king - ly in Thy meek-ness, Thou

Son of God, Thou Son of God. Glo - ry and

hon - our: Let the world di - vide and take them; Crown its mon - archs and un -

- make them; But Thou, ... Thou wilt reign.

Here in a - base - ment; Crown - less,

poor, dis - robed, and bleed - ing: There, in

glo - ry in - ter - ced - ing, Thou art the King, Thou art the King!

cres. molto.

There, in glo-ry in-ter-ced-ing, there, in glo-ry in-ter-ced - ing, Thou art the

King, Thou art the King, Thou art the King!

No. 8.　　　Recit.—AND AS MOSES LIFTED UP THE SERPENT.

Slow. **Bass.** *cres.*

And　as　Mo - ses　　lift - ed up　the ser-pent in the

Slow. ♩ = 66.

wil - der-ness,　e - ven　so　must the　Son　of　Man　be　lift - ed up;

Andante. *p*

that who - so - ev - er　be - liev - eth　in　Him,　that　who - so -

Andante. ♩ = 90.

p legato sempre.

- ev - er　be - liev - eth　in　Him　　should　not　per - ish,

cres. *f* *rall.*

should　not　per - ish,　but　have　ev - er - last - ing　life.

cres. *rall.*

Attacca.

No. 9. Quartet or Chorus (*Unaccompanied*).—GOD SO LOVED THE WORLD.

have ev - er - last - ing life. For God sent not His Son in - to the

have ev - er - last - ing life. For God sent not His Son in - to the

have ev - er - last - ing life. For God sent not His Son in - to the

have ev - er - last - ing life.

world to con - demn the world, God sent not His Son in - to the world to con -

world to con - demn the world, God sent not His Son in - to the world to con -

world to con - demn the world, God sent not His Son in - to the world to con -

God sent not His Son in - to the world to con -

- demn the world; but that the world through Him might be sa - - ved.

- demn the world; but that the world through Him might be sa - - ved.

- demn the world; but that the world through Him might be sa - - ved.

- demn the world; but that the world through Him might be sa - - ved.

God so loved the world, . . God so loved the world, . . that He
gave His on-ly be-got-ten Son, that who-so be-liev-eth, be-
liev-eth in Him should not per-ish, should not per-ish, but

have ev - er - last - ing life, ev - er - last - ing,
cres.
have ev - er - last - ing life, ev - er - last - ing life, ev - er - last - ing,
cres.
have ev - er - last - ing life, ev er - last - ing life, ev - er - last - ing,
cres.
have ev - er - last - ing life, ev - er - last - ing life, ev - er - last - ing,
cres.
dim. rall. pp
ev - er - last - ing life. God so loved the world, . .
dim. rall. pp
ev - er last - ing life. God so loved the world,
dim. rall. pp
ev - er - last - ing life. God so loved the world. . .
dim. rall. pp
ev - er - last - ing life. God so loved the world, . .
dim. rall.
pp
ppp rall.
God so loved the world, . . . God so loved the world.
ppp rall.
God so loved the world, . . . God so loved the world.
ppp rall.
God so loved the world, . . . God so loved the world.
ppp rall.
God so loved the world, . . . God so loved the world.
ppp rall.

No. 10.   LITANY OF THE PASSION.

To be sung by the Choir and Congregation.

Cru - ci - fied, I turn to Thee, Son of Ma - ry, plead for me.

HOLY Jesu, by Thy passion,
　By the woes which none can share,
Borne in more than kingly fashion,
　By Thy love beyond compare :
　　Crucified, I turn to Thee,
　　Son of Mary, plead for me.

By the treachery and trial,
　By the blows and sore distress,
By desertion and denial,
　By Thine awful loneliness :
　　Crucified, I turn to Thee,
　　Son of Mary, plead for me.

By Thy look so sweet and lowly,
　While they smote Thee on the Face,
By Thy patience, calm and holy,
　In the midst of keen disgrace :
　　Crucified, I turn to Thee,
　　Son of Mary, plead for me.

By the hour of condemnation,
　By the blood which trickled down,
When, for us and our salvation,
　Thou didst wear the robe and crown :
　　Crucified, I turn to Thee,
　　Son of Mary, plead for me.

By the path of sorrows dreary,
　By the Cross, Thy dreadful load,
By the pain, when, faint and weary,
　Thou didst sink upon the road :
　　Crucified, I turn to Thee,
　　Son of Mary, plead for me.

By the Spirit which could render
　Love for hate and good for ill,
By the mercy, sweet and tender,
　Poured upon Thy murderers still :
　　Crucified, I turn to Thee,
　　Son of Mary, plead for me.

STAND

No. 11. Recit.—JESUS SAID, "FATHER FORGIVE THEM."

Tenor Solo.

Slow.

Je - sus

Slow. ♩ = about 66.

p Sw.

senza Ped.

Chorus. Tenors and Basses.

said: "Fa-ther, for-give them; for they know not what . . . they do."

Gt. soft Diap.

No. 12. Duet.—SO THOU LIFTEST THY DIVINE PETITION.

Andante. ♩ = 70.

Solo.

p

pp Sw.

senza Ped.

Bass.

So Thou lift-est Thy di - vine pe - ti - tion, Pierc'd with cru-el an-guish through and through;

p

cres.

dim.

senza Ped.

Tenor.

A little slower.

So Thou grievest o'er our lost con - di - tion, Pleading, "Ah, they know not what they do."

A little slower.

Bass. expression.
Oh! 'twas love,
rall.
dim.
pp
Tenor.
a tempo.
Oh! 'twas love, in love's di-vi-nest fea-ture, Pass-ing o'er that
cres.
f
dim.
in love's di-vi-nest fea-ture, Pass-ing o'er that
a tempo.
mf
dark and murd'rous blot, Though they slay Thee—
dark and murd'rous blot, Find-ing, e'en for each low-fall-en crea-ture,
p rit.
one re-deem-ing spot.
Though they slay Thee—one re-deem-ing spot.
rit.
L.H.
tempo.

A little slower; with devotion. *cres.* *dim.*

Yes! and still Thy pa-tient Heart is yearn-ing

A little slower. ♩ = 60 to 62.

rall. *p* *cres.* *dim.*

p *cres.* *mf*

With a love that mor-tal scarce can bear;

p

Thou in Pi - ty, deep, divine, and burn - ing,

p *cres.* *mf* *p*

poco rit. ten. cres. a tempo.

E'en for me, e'en for me Thy might - y, .. might - y prayer.

poco rit. ten. *cres. a tempo.*

Lift - est e'en for me, e'en for me Thy might - y, .. might - y prayer.

poco rit. *ten.* *ten.* *a tempo.*

p

p *cres.* *mf*

So Thou pleadest, e'en for my transgres-sion, Bid-ding me look up and trust and live;

cres. *mf* *dim.*

soft Ped. *senza Ped.*

8002.

So Thou mur-murest Thine in - ter - ces - sion, Bid-ding me look up and trust and live;

So Thou plead - est, Yea, he knew not, yea, he knew not—for

So Thou plead - est, Yea, he knew not, yea, he knew not—for

My sake, for - give, for My sake, for - give, for - give, for - give.

My sake, for - give, for My sake, for - give, for - give, for - give.

No. 13.   THE MYSTERY OF INTERCESSION.

To be sung by the Choir and Congregation.

Jesus, the Crucified, pleads for me,
While He is nailed to the shameful tree,
Scorned and forsaken, derided and curst,
See how His enemies do their worst!
Yet, in the midst of the torture and shame,
Jesus, the Crucified, breathes my name!
Wonder of wonders, oh! how can it be?
Jesus, the Crucified, pleads for me!

Lord, I have left Thee, I have denied,
Followed the world in my selfish pride;
Lord, I have joined in the hateful cry,
Slay Him, away with Him, crucify!
Lord, I have done it, oh! ask me not how;
Woven the thorns for Thy tortured Brow:
Yet in His pity so boundless and free,
Jesus, the Crucified, pleads for me!

Though thou hast left Me and wandered away,
Chosen the darkness instead of the day;
Though thou art covered with many a stain,
Though thou hast wounded Me oft and again:
Though thou hast followed thy wayward will;
Yet, in My pity, I love thee still.
Wonder of wonders it ever must be!
Jesus, the Crucified, pleads for me!

Jesus is dying, in agony sore,
Jesus is suffering more and more,
Jesus is bowed with the weight of His woe,
Jesus is faint with each bitter throe.
Jesus is bearing it all in my stead,
Pity Incarnate for me has bled;
Wonder of wonders it ever must be
Jesus, the Crucified, pleads for me!

No. 14. RECIT.—AND ONE OF THE MALEFACTORS.

Slow. **BASS.** *ad lib.*

And one of the mal - e-factors which were hang - ed, railed on Him, say - ing,

A VOICE IN THE CHOIR. *mf*

"If Thou be the Christ, save Thyself and us."

BASS SOLO. *Slow.* STRICT.

But the o - ther, an-swer-ing, re - bu - ked him,

ANOTHER VOICE. *mf Quicker.*

say - ing, "Dost not thou fear God, see-ing thou art in the same con-dem - na - tion? And we in-deed just - ly; for we re-ceive the due re-

-ward of our deeds: but this man hath done no-thing a - miss." And he

Slow. VOICE IN CHOIR.

said un - to Je - sus, "Lord, re - mem-ber me when Thou com - est

BASS SOLO.

in - to Thy King - - dom." And Je - sus said un - to him,

TENORS.

"Ver - i - ly I say to thee, to-day shalt thou be with Me . . in Pa - ra - dise."

BASSES.

"Ver - i - ly I say to thee, to-day shalt thou be with Me . . in Par - ra - dise."

Slow.

No. 15.   THE ADORATION OF THE CRUCIFIED.

To be sung by the Choir and Congregation.

I ADORE Thee, I adore Thee!
Glorious ere the world began;
Yet more wonderful Thou shinest,
Though divine, yet still divinest
In Thy dying love for man.

I adore Thee, I adore Thee!
Thankful at Thy feet to be;
I have heard Thy accent thrilling,
Lo! I come, for Thou art willing
Me to pardon, even me.

I adore Thee, I adore Thee!
Born of woman yet Divine:
Stained with sins I kneel before Thee,
Sweetest Jesu, I implore Thee
Make me ever only Thine.

STANO

No. 16. RECIT.—WHEN JESUS THEREFORE SAW HIS MOTHER.

When Je - sus there - fore saw His Mo - ther, and the dis - ci - ple stand - ing by, whom He lov - ed, He saith un - to His Mo - ther, "Wo - man, be - hold thy son!" Then saith He to the dis - ci - ple, "Be - hold thy mo - ther!"

"Wo - man, be - hold thy son!"

"Be - hold thy mo - ther!"

Ped. 16 ft. & soft 8 ft.

Adagio.

Adagio.

legato.

BASS SOLO. *ad lib.*

There was darkness o-ver all the land.

And at the ninth hour Je-sus cried with a loud voice, say-ing,

Adagio.
CHORUS. TENORS.
mf

"My God, My God, why hast Thou for-sa-ken Me?"

BASSES.
mf

"My God, My God, why hast Thou for-sa-ken Me?"

Adagio.

mf

CHOIR STAND

No. 17.   Recit.—IS IT NOTHING TO YOU?

Is it no-thing to you, all ye that pass by? Be-hold, and see if there be a - ny sor-row like un-to My sor-row, which is done un-to Me, where-with the Lord hath af - flict - ed Me in the day of His fierce an - ger.

No. 18.   THE APPEAL OF THE CRUCIFIED.

ye that pass by? I laid My e-ter-nal power a-side, I came from the

Home of the Glo - ri - fied, A babe, in the low - ly cave to

lie; Is it no-thing to you, all ye that pass by?

I wept for the sor-rows and pains of men, I healed them, and

I wept for the sor-rows and pains of men, I healed them, and

I wept for the sor-rows and pains of men, I healed them, and

I wept for the sor-rows and pains of men, I healed them, and

helped them, and loved them— but then, but then

helped them, and loved . . them— but then, but then

helped them, and loved them— but then, but then

helped them, and loved them— but then, but then

Ped.

They shout - ed a - gainst Me— "Cru - ci-fy!

They shout - ed a - gainst Me— "Cru - ci-fy!

They shout - ed a - gainst Me— "Cru - ci-fy!

"Cru - ci-fy! Cru - ci-fy!

fff
Cru-ci-fy! Cru - ci - fy!"
Cru-ci-fy! Cru-ci-fy! Cru - ci - fy!"
Cru-ci-fy! Cru - ci - fy!"
Cru-ci-fy! Cru - ci - fy!"
pp
a tempo.
Is it no-thing to you? Be-hold Me and see:
It is no-thing to you? Be-hold Me and see:
Is it no-thing to you? Be-hold Me and see:
Is it no-thing to you? Be-hold Me and see:
p a tempo.
cres.
f
ff
pierc-ed through and through With count - less sor-rows—and all is for you; For
pierc-ed through and through With count - less sor-rows—and all is for you; For
pierc-ed through and through With count - less sor-rows—and all is for you; For
pierc-ed through and through With count - less sor-rows—and all is for you; For

you I suf-fer, for you I die, Is it no-thing to

you I suf-fer, for you I die, Is it no-thing to

you I suf-fer, for you I die, Is it no-thing to

you I suf-fer, for you I die, Is it no-thing to

con Ped.

you, all ye that pass by? Oh!

you, all ye that pass by? Oh!

you, all ye that pass by? Oh!

you, all ye that pass by? Oh!

men and wo-men, your deeds of shame, Your sins with-out rea - son and

men and wo-men, your deeds of shame, Your sins with out .. rea - son and

men and wo-men, your deeds of shame, Your sins with-out .. rea - son and

men and wo-men, your deeds of shame, Your sins with-out rea - son and num-ber and name; I bear them all on the Cross on high;

num-ber and name; I bear them all on the Cross on high;

num-ber and name; I bear them all on the Cross on high;

num-ber and name; I bear them all on the Cross on high;

f Accomp. ad lib.

Org. p

Is it no-thing to you? Is it no-thing to you that I

Is it no-thing to you? Is it no-thing to you that I

Is it no-thing to you? Is it no-thing to you that I

Is it no-thing to you? Is it no-thing to you that I

cres.

mf

bow My Head? And no-thing to you that My Blood is shed? O

bow My Head? And no-thing to you that My Blood is shed? O

bow My Head? And no-thing to you that My Blood is shed? O

bow My Head? And no-thing to you that My Blood is shed? O

cres.

mf

per-ish-ing souls to you I cry, Is it no-thing to you?

per-ish-ing souls to you I cry, Is it no-thing to you?

per-ish-ing souls to you I cry, Is it no-thing to you?

per-ish-ing souls to you I cry, Is it no-thing to you?

O come un-to Me, O come un-to Me, O

O come un-to Me, O come un-to Me, O

O come un-to Me, O come un-to Me, O

O come un-to Me, O come un-to Me,

come un-to Me— by the woes I have borne, By the dread-ful scourge, and the

come un-to Me— by the woes I have borne, By the dread-ful scourge, and the

come un-to Me— by the woes I have borne, By the dread-ful scourge, and the

come un-to Me— by the woes I have borne, By the dread-ful scourge, and the crown of thorns, By these, I im - plore you to hear My cry, Is it

crown of thorns, By these, I im - plore you to hear My cry, Is it

crown of thorns, By these, I im - plore you to hear My cry, Is it

crown of thorns, By these, I im - plore you to hear My cry, Is it

no-thing to you? O come un-to Me, O come un-to Me, O

no-thing to you? O come un-to Me, O come un-to Me, O

no-thing to you? O come un-to Me, O come un-to Me, O

no-thing to you? O come un-to Me, O come un-to Me, O

come un-to Me—.. this aw-ful price, Re-demp-tion's tre-men-dous

come un-to Me— this aw-ful price, Re-demp-tion's tre-men-dous

come un-to Me— this aw-ful price, Re-demp-tion's tre-men-dous

come un-to Me— this aw-ful price, Re-demp-tion's tre-men-dous sac - ri - fice— Is paid for you, is paid for you— Oh,

why will ye die? O come un-to Me, O come un-to Me, O

come un-to Me—.. For why will ye die, for why will ye die? O come, . . . O come, . . . O come un-to Me! Why,

come, . . . O come, . . . O come un-to Me! Why,

come, . . . O come, . . . O come un-to Me! Why,

come, . . . O come, . . . O come un-to Me! Why,

why will ye die? Come un-to Me, come un-to Me, come

why will ye die? Come un-to Me, come un-to Me, come, O..

why will ye die? Come un-to Me, come un-to Me, come, O..

why will ye die? Come un-to Me? come un-to Me, come

to Me.

come un-to Me.

come un-to Me.

to Me. *Vox Angelica.*

pp ad lib.

No. 19. RECIT. AND CHORUS.—AFTER THIS, JESUS KNOWING THAT
ALL THINGS WERE NOW ACCOMPLISHED.

Je - sus had re - ceiv - ed the vin - e - gar, He saith,

CHORUS. TENORS.
Very slow.

"It is fin - ish - ed. Fa - ther, in - to Thy hands I com -

BASSES.

"It is fin - ish - ed. Fa - ther, in - to Thy hands I com -

Very slow.

TENOR SOLO.

And He bowed His Head, and gave up the ghost.

- mend My spi - rit."

NO TURN

- mend My spi - rit."

No. 20.

FOR THE LOVE OF JESUS.

To be sung by the Choir and Congregation.

ALL for Jesus—all for Jesus,
   This our song shall ever be;
For we have no hope, nor Saviour,
   If we have not hope in Thee.

All for Jesus—Thou wilt give us
   Strength to serve Thee, hour by hour;
None can move us from Thy presence,
   While we trust Thy love and power.

All for Jesus—at Thine altar
   Thou wilt give us sweet content;
There, dear Lord, we shall receive Thee
   In the solemn Sacrament.

All for Jesus—Thou hast loved us;
   All for Jesus—Thou hast died;
All for Jesus—Thou art with us;
   All for Jesus Crucified.

All for Jesus—all for Jesus—
   This the Church's song must be;
Till, at last, her sons are gathered
   One in love and one in Thee.

A - men.

THE END.